SINGLE-SENTENCE STORIES

Single-Sentence Stories

Harold Jaffe
and
Tom Whalen

SPUYTEN DUYVIL

New York City

© 2023 Harold Jaffe, Tom Whalen
ISBN 978-1-959556-76-3
Cover: *Canto VI*, Barnett Newman, 1963

Library of Congress Control Number: 2023037119

for Félix Fénéon, predecessor

Fragrance is the flower's echo

　　　—Ramon Gomez de la Serna

EXCHANGE

A doomed Jew and a doomed priest changed positions, the priest having volunteered to take the Jew's place in the Nazi deathcamp so that the Jew could mark the solemn day of Yom Kippur; the priest was gassed, then two days after Yom Kippur the Jew was gassed.

DESPAIR & POETRY

John Berger writes of the besieged Palestinians' *despair without fear*, which would have to be the most unrelenting despair there is, and perhaps the making of the deepest poetry.

SISTERS

I gaze at a photo of two young women who would resemble sisters if they weren't wearing opposing "uniforms": one Palestinian, the other Israeli, both Semites, neither white; before the night is over one of them will blow up a bus on a suicide mission.

THE YOUNG MOTHERS

The young mothers gather in the morning in the cafes of Stuttgart-West to talk about the state of motherhood, the consensus being that it is not what it should be, though to the eavesdropper they're radiant with life, as they discuss, over their cappuccinos and brioches, the difficulties besetting them.

DANCING FORBIDDEN

An Iranian court has handed jail sentences of more than 10 years each to a young couple who danced in front of one of Tehran's main landmarks in a video seen as a symbol of defiance against the regime.

HIJAB

I remember a sunny day in my 20s when a white male colleague asked me if I would like to take off my hijab; I looked at his sweltering, red face and smiled: "Yes, it is a bit hot: if you remove your trousers, I'll take off my hijab."

WARSAW GHETTO

Around 260,000 were deported from the ghetto to the Treblinka extermination camp and murdered; after mass deportations in 1942, those remaining inside the ghetto began to make preparations for an uprising, smuggling in weapons and explosives.

ANTI-MEMORY

Holocaust memory has become a contentious topic in today's Poland, where the nationalist government has tried to criminalize attributing any responsibility to the Polish nation for the Holocaust, and sought to focus on cases of Poles who helped Jews.

I'LL SWEAR BY THAT

Correspondent Robert Fisk: "Reporters should be neutral and unbiased on the side of those who suffer."

SHE'S OUR SISTER

Creaturely, she waddled into the midst of heavy traffic
and commenced to remove her hoodie
then a sweatshirt
another sweatshirt
a torn jersey
another jersey
a tee shirt
laying them in a pile on the maddening freeway, ignoring
the horns and hoots.

CENTERING

I was suffering deeply when I had this dream:
A sacred voice whispered: Center on the sound *a-u-m*
without any *a* or *m*.

CARRIERS OF MIRRORS

Only those who carry mirrors on their backs may cross the road now.

FAIL BETTER

Only by failing utterly can you be free to create, she insisted.

NOTHIN' LEFT

If you fail "utterly" ain't nothin' left.

TIRESIAS

None of them could see the color of the sky—except for one & he was sightless.

UH-HUH

When you stretch out both legs and sleep, there is neither a "false" nor a "true."

PROPHECIES WITHHELD

Black Elk, the Oglala Sioux shaman, resisted his prophetic dreams, as did Tiresias and Cassandra, whose fate was to be prophetic but discredited.

PROPHECIES UNHEEDED

Rebellion of the hanged = revolution of the just.

I'LL STAY WITH MY FLAT STONES

Scientists now claim that heavier, potato-shaped rather than flatter, stones can produce "almighty" leaps out of the water.

KICK & GIGGLE

One juvenile says: "We gonna kick the bum in the back, then we gonna kick his face in; when we done the bum's gonna know what it feels like to get fucked over real good"—then both juves giggle.

COMEDY OF REMARRIAGE

A husband suspects his wife grew from the seed of a foreigner at the same time the wife senses her husband is a foreigner eager to drain her of her essence, and in this way they live together for nineteen years, on the outside a normal couple, on the inside distrustful and filled with hate, until they divorce, only to meet in a bar a year later and over a few drinks admit their true feelings toward one another, learning each thought the other a foreigner, and thus realize as foreigners they have more in common than they thought, that in fact they love one another after all, and so they remarry, only to suspect shortly thereafter that somewhere there was a flaw in their logic, she's even more foreign than he thought and he's ditto, the moral of which you can write for yourself since I'm too depressed to think about it.

THEN WHAT?

Put snow in a silver bowl,
hide a heron in the light of the moon.

INTRODUCTION TO COSMOLOGY

Our father dragged my brother and me into a field, handed each of us a branch the size of a baseball bat, and had us beat one another until we saw stars.

SPRAYING

Shortly after 10 pm an employee entered a break room at the back of the store where staff were gathering at the start of the overnight shift, and according to an eyewitness, "just started spraying"; the gunman used a Glock semiautomatic to shoot his victims then turned the weapon on himself—within seconds.

AMERICAN LESSONS IN DYING #63

Try to acknowledge the full loss of each American killed by guns during any given month in the United States and see how far you get with that and where it takes you.

THE "GOLDEN STATE"

California police were more than twice as likely to use force against Black residents than white residents during traffic and pedestrian stops in 2021, according to a new report on racial profiling.

SO LET'S REVERT TO COLONIZATION

Africa is <u>less safe, secure and democratic</u> than a decade ago, experts agree.

MILITARY-INDUSTRIAL COMPLEX

A war between China and Taiwan will be extremely profitable for business at America's Frontier Fund, a tech investment outfit whose co-founder and CEO sits on both the State Department Foreign Affairs Policy Board and President Joe Biden's Intelligence Advisory Board, according to the transcript from a February 1 event.

VIOLENT RAPTURE

Skillful warriors will use the force of momentum to
seize victory without having to exert their strength; they
then lie back and smoke the pipe of rapture.

A SENTENCE FOR CHOMSKY

For two hours in the late morning of 24 March 2010 I heard a talk by Noam Chomsky solely on linguistics to an overflow crowd, with him citing the literature in the field as if there were nothing in linguistics, not a single paper, he hadn't read, and responding gracefully and forcefully to the questions and comments of the young linguistics professors and graduate students from Tübingen, Erlangen, Stuttgart, Munich eager to draw sustenance from the old anarchist.

REMEMBER 2 REMEMBER

Chomsky is 94 now and has naturally forgotten a vast encyclopedia of knowledge which leaves a dozen vast encyclopedias that he remembers word for word—at least that's what is claimed, though not by Chomsky.

NOW IT BEGINS

Gentlemen, the old age pensioner said, I don't know what's happening to me.

TOLSTOY

There is an honorable old age, there is a miserable old age, there is a pitiable old age, there is also an old age that is both honorable and miserable.

SURREAL

At moments his blood flows the wrong way, but he has become used to it.

PAIRS

I often think of artistic brilliance in pairs: Graham
Greene and Max Frisch; Roman Polanski and Charles
Manson; Clarice Lispector and Emily Dickinson; Andrei
Tarkovsky and Robert Bresson; Theodore Kaczynski
and Jerzy Kosinski; Goya and Van Gogh; Lewis Carroll
and Balthus; Brando and Belmondo; Nina Simone and
Jeanne Moreau; Kathy Acker and Anais Nin; Egon
Schiele and Otto Dix; Tristan Tzara is melded in my
imagination with Jean-Luc Godard—they never met.

HAMMETT

Last night I re-watched Heisler's *The Glass Key* (1942),
with Ladd and Lake (impossible to decide which one is
the prettier; alas, both came to bad ends), and noticed
how it partook of some of the source's sadism, which
Kurosawa perhaps drew from the film for the scenes
where Mifune gets the shit beaten out of him in *Yojimbo*,
also sourced from a Hammett novel, *Red Harvest*.

TOUGH TINY

Veronica Lake, Alan Ladd's frequent co-star, was marginally more delectable than Alan Ladd—and taller; Ladd is listed as five-feet-seven, but my sources tell me he was more like five-feet-three in shoes; and he could grapple—look at how he handled the six-foot-four Jack Palance in *Shane*.

EXTREME CRUELTY

The director of *Caché*, the Austrian Haneke, is somehow indebted to extreme cruelty which he funnels into his films; I especially object to Haneke employing African characters whom he knows nothing about except through his research; in *Caché* he has Majid, one of the main Algerians, slit his throat in front of the audience, as though self-mutilation was endemic to certain "primitive" folk.

B TRAVEN

Every one of B Traven's serious novels, each written in German, has to do with the victimization of the impoverished Indians; we witness this clearly in his six "Jungle Novels," beginning with *La Carreta* and ending with *The General from the Jungle*; the Indians suffer until they learn to respond collectively with an avenging, unremitting violence against their oppressors.

TELEGENIC CHE

In 2001 I traveled to Havana to interview Alberto Korda, who photographed the revolutionary Cubans around the world; it was Korda who snapped the famous photo of Che in his beret with the red star in the center; though Korda's photo was taken in Cuba in 1960 it became well-known only in 1967 when Che was betrayed and assassinated in Bolivia, with his wrists and ankles severed.

KILL PEOPLE

Ideas don't kill people, people kill people; landmines don't kill people, people kill people; bullets don't kill people, people kill people; guns don't kill people, people kill people; hurricanes don't kill people, people kill people; toxins don't kill people, people kill people; God doesn't kill people, people kill people; dreams don't kill people, people kill people; planes don't kill people, people kill people; surmises don't kill people, people kill people; smiles don't kill people, people kill people; detective novels don't kill people, people kill people; horses don't kill people, people kill people; swimming pools don't kill people, people kill people; insecticides don't kill people, people kill people; missiles don't kill people, people kill people; fires don't kill people, people kill people; cancers don't kill people, people kill people; false histories don't kill people, people kill people; laws don't kill people, people kill people; peepholes don't kill people, people kill people.

PSYCHOPATH

"You are courteous, even modest, in real time," she says, "but in your writings you are a psychopath"; she is on point and I thank her.

SIR MICK

Salman Rushdie, gravely injured after his recent attack while on stage, and with the Fatwa evidently still pending, has, it seems, finally paid his debt for the extraordinary early success of *Midnight's Children* and his being knighted; come to think of it, Mick Jagger has just been knighted—and eminently deserved.

KAFTAN

I am always happiest when my kids are in good form and we are having a lovely family dinner without any intruder disguised as a Muslim in a kaftan who insists on squeezing my boob.

BELLOWING

Language is to the felt mind what law is to justice:
bellowing of elephants, weeping of dolphins, grief-song
the calf sings to her mother murdered for ivory; I call
those bereaved sounds anti-language.

THE ZOO AT NIGHT

Sometimes, after my husband has gone to sleep and the revelers have returned to their homes, I step out into the river of the street and let it take me to the zoo where the animals, freed from the labors of their day, recall the dust from which they came, and it's at this moment, when their eyes rock on the last wave of consciousness, that they become aware of my presence—the axolotl clings to its glass, the bison rumbles up from the ground, the anteater unfolds it arms and stands like the great bear it is—and in the line of their gaze I roll up like an urchin, cease all movement, all thought, until I wake in bed beside this man whose body, like the one I live in, I've known too long.

WITHOUT BLINKING

Mad Artaud was asked to present a radio speech to cultivated France; for four hours, the story goes, he stood before the microphone not uttering a word: cultivated France listened without blinking.

HAND WRITING

My hand wants to write sentences that in no sense belong to me or who I take me to be, the me, that is, who would never write what my hand wants me to write, and

without my willing it, my eyes want to read what I myself would never want to read, much less write or imagine writing or see in print, and

now realize that I've only seen my eyes in reflection, never in reality, so I shouldn't worry about what my eyes want to read, should I,

but the reflection wants to see me as that which I've never been and never wanted to be, in order, perhaps, to observe me performing acts I've no desire or intention to perform, much less imagine

ART BRUT

Is the brut (or "psychotic") artist's art restorative or does it intensify the torment?

MAGIC DISEASE

The same psychic states which, in India or New Guinea, are valued for their magic power, are declared to be diseased in our society and penalized by exclusion or confinement. (Foucault)

BREAKDOWN / BREAKTHROUGH

Psychosis is often generated by an agonizing breakdown, which, at the same time, liberates an immense creative potential. (RD Laing)

CLAW-LIKE

Even though I no longer suffer from the disease, people insist on viewing me as a leper, he said, displaying a discolored claw-like left hand.

BLOODIED

You fear to feel but your mind is bloodied with feeling.

SQUEEZE DON'T SQUEEZE

Zed wanted to kill himself but he didn't want to do it to himself because if he killed himself it might be sinful but if someone else put the .38 to his left temple and pulled the trigger maybe he wouldn't go to hell or wherever is down there; that sounds stupid and Zed wasn't stupid.

FRAU HIMMELBLAU'S DILEMMA

"Should we release him from his misery or let him suffer or make him suffer even more, as if life were only a power thing, you know, but without trophies, without trophies …," Frau Himmelblau kept repeating, until her granddaughter put both her and grandfather out of their misery.

FOOLS & CAMO

Had I been more familiar with the country's ways I would have realized that I was unsafe at any time in any place; I should have disguised myself to look like the fools who wore camo and flashily displayed their guns and axes.

GAME OF THE CENTURY

In the fall of 1969, after Nixon helicoptered in to watch the Longhorns against the Razorbacks, Fayetteville erupted in violence, and the next day I saw cars with Texas license plates overturned, their windshields busted, but at least now the buildings were free of the Secret Service agents who had been eying us through binoculars from rooftops and windows the week prior to Nixon's arrival.

UNCONSOLED

Long into the night I listen to voices nattering now in one tongue, now another *You shouldn't listen to us but to what it is that makes* you *you, but in what sense can you claim to be who you say you are* as I toss and turn, long into the night, pondering the hard truths of my past.

COMMON ERROR

Please don't mistake my idiosyncrasies for character, he said.

PARC DE BELLEVILLE

It was there that my mother was accosted one day when she was out by herself in the Parc de Belleville and kissed full on the mouth by a murderous type.

POOR CHILD

Ah, poor child, there's nothing I can do with your present sorrow or what's to come, there's no moon out tonight, all the other workers have gone home to their wives and children, to their husbands, their empty homes, their parents, their nurses, and only you and I are here on this corner, and I can't help you, not me, I can do nothing with the beauty that grows inside you like a cancer, there's nothing that can take it out of you, no one has a scalpel that can do that.

LORD BYRON

Byron's increasing baldness, his tendency to fat, and his decaying teeth depressed him; no doubt he felt they made him markedly less attractive to the boys in the convent, so why not die a martyr's death while fighting with the Greeks against . . .

EVERYBODY'S LITTLE PROBLEMS

While Mary was licking her fingers, the conductor was beating the band, and I had the uncanny feeling that someone was looking at me through a microscope.

WHERE'S VENUS?

Our slender Adonis is dying
tear open your dresses
oh virgins, batter your breasts!

SOMETHING AMISS

Every day I come to the Hegelhaus, the house where
Hegel was born, every day that it's open, I wander the
exhibit rooms upstairs, then sit down at a table on the
second floor, with the plush pillow in view upon which
Hegel sat, and write whatever comes to mind, like today
I remember K. and I had just made popcorn, we're about
to watch a DVD or old television series, *Route 66* or *The
Fugitive*, something, I don't remember, and I'm washing
the pan so we won't have it to do afterwards, and she
says, "Why do you do that, why do you always want to
wash things before we've even eaten?" and I say because
…, but then I realize something has gone amiss, a cell,
a toggle, some neural disturbance, and that no matter
what I say, I'm no longer who I was.

ENTIRE SAHARA

I tried to stand back from my obsession with the river, but already I was thinking of the irrigation of the entire Sahara—the transformation of the desert into the Edenic paradise envisioned so precisely in my dreams.

RESISTANCE TO TRUTH

In the resistance to truth we may enter a door that is not a door and fall through a floor that is not a floor past the dead who are not dead into an afterlife that is not an afterlife, but I wouldn't call it a life either.

AND THE HEART?

The brain, FYI, smells of fish.

AN INCONVENIENT BET

In the first place, Ribault knew he couldn't lose, never had, never would, then placed what was left of his chips on 19 black.

BLACK IS BLACK

I am tall, slender, rather melancholy, I dress meticulously but always in black, I drink only after 4 pm and I don't visit brothels, but I like ladies, and ladies do not dislike me.

FYI

Hashish provokes amusement / opium courtesy.

SCREEN

While G talked, Zed had approached the screen, which displayed a white police officer with his semi-automatic flush against a Black adolescent's cheek; "and what does *this* mean?" Zed demanded.

EXPLANATION

"Explanations come to an end somewhere," she insisted.

NEVER AGAIN

My close friends know how I strike out violently because it pains and angers me that they will never again be born, never again be young on this earth.

PANDEMIC

In every eye of every child, as they stare into their iPalm,
a bright dot shrinks to a quantum speck, then drifts down,
irretrievable, into the darkness therein.

SERGEI EISENSTEIN

Excerpts from five Shostakovich's symphonies accompanied Eisenstein's controversial masterpiece *Battleship Potemkin,* 1925.

TROTSKY WAS JEWISH

Leon Trotsky, murdered in Mexico by a NKVD agent, was one of the few Stalin rivals to not be rehabilitated by either Nikita Khrushchev or Mikhail Gorbachev.

AL-AL-ALGORITHM

From my mother's sleep I fell into the Algorithm:
digital Hades, infant investors selling their shitty diapers
to an NFT—don't grin, it's big, big crypto.

METASTASIZING AI

AI is moving with lightning speed in virtually every domain, including art-making: We must review reforms to intellectual property law, strengthen the rights of performers and artists, and take action to support the creative sector in adapting to the disruptions caused by swift and convulsive technological change.

GERRYMANDERING

She shot him twice in the chest after he proudly confessed to gerrymandering in order to deny immigrant-citizens the right to vote their choice of mayor—it being Alabama, she was sentenced to death.

THE ATTACK

Though I did not know when the attack began or whether it traveled by air or sound, I knew from the moment I laid my head on the pillow that it had begun.

REAL ICE WATER

Moreover, you get ice water to drink and as much as you want, but above all you get edible food, with plate, knife, fork, spoon on a table that might have been crudely knocked together but is a table all the same, and there is a real bench to sit on.

ON BELIEF

Again and again a fit comes upon us and we believe in the probability that we believe in belief as if it were a validation ticket to eternity, but suppose you drank this glass on the table before it was filled and then suppose that the legs of the table vanished but the table top neither fell nor wobbled, then what would you think of saving first, the glass on the table or your belief that you are not dreaming?

MAD POETRY

Verlaine, carrying a large fish and a bottle of Sancerre, had a hop in his step as he walked to the decrepit building in Soho where Rimbaud was looking through the window and laughing at him: "You look like a proper fool!"

VERLAINE INTERFACE

Today, 11 June 2015, my horoscope said, "An intense encounter turns into a nightmare of novelistic proportions," but until that happened I knew I could live on the pure happiness of my shortcomings.

RAW FISH & POETRY

When Verlaine got upstairs he slapped Rimbaud in the face with the raw fish, then slammed the door and left; the next time they met Verlaine shot Rimbaud with a pistol but only wounded him.

A PROFESSION OF LOVE

Few carve their names or initials or professions of love on park benches anymore, because the slats we sit on are not made from wood, but from plastic recycled in China.

PANDEMIC SOUP

If you are infected with one of these new variants, you should also have strong protection to the rest of the soup; still, it is advised that you sip with a spoon, metaphorically speaking.

THE LITTLE GOLDEN KEY

"... but, alas! the little door was shut again, and the little golden key was lying on the glass table as before ..." (L. Carroll)

NEXT BEND

Remove your spectacles:

bleak is bleak

we're fucked irreparably

death is at the next bend for everyone

except maybe trillionaires colonizing Pluto

SF

Day after day he reads science fiction, one book after another—*Garbage World*, *The Moon Pool*, *The Dreaming Jewels*: "And while the garbage world exploded ... while a thousand sterile pleasure worlds cowered before a vast cloud of filth ..." etc.

ASYMMETRY

Mahayana Buddhism cites the void and compassion as inherent in the world however degraded the world has become; their void is a vibrating emptiness such as the asymmetrical spaces between the rocks in Ryoan-ji in Kyoto.

SILENT & BRILLIANT

Sun, my relative, be silent and brilliant going down at
sunset so that we sleep quietly and wake the next dawn
feeling good.

PSYCHO-SAINT

I can't help thinking of an affectionately satirical film about Saint Francis by the Neorealist director Rossellini; am I permitted to say that like Roberto Rossellini's Saint Francis you are either a clown, a psychotic, or a species of saint—possibly something in between?

THE PREY

They had caught the scent of my loneliness, yes, that's what it was, and now were here to feed on it, to draw their strength from my weakness.

I PREFER CAMELS

Officials from the Obion county sheriff's office said the fatal incident unfolded around 5.44 pm on Thursday, when they "received a call of a loose camel near Shirley Farms on South Bluff Road in Obion … attacking people."

FOREST IN FOG

When she requested he cease all contact, he immediately agreed, not wanting to distress this person who for half a year nursed an injured hedgehog she had saved from a fox's mouth back to health before releasing it into the Kräherwald, a small forest in northwest Stuttgart where one autumn morning three decades ago I lost my way in a fog.

ZEBRAS & CAMELS

Three years ago, in July 2019, an inspector reported that: "the only access to drinking water for the camels and zebras was a very small shallow muddy creek running through their enclosure; there was no access to any water troughs or other potable water source."

THE 26TH EXCRETION

"The twenty-sixth excretion of man is himself."
    – C. Enzensberger

REPTILIAN

Reptilian mega-billionaire space tourist Jeff Bezos bought the Washington Post for a mere $250m, less that 1% of what dysmorphic manchild Elon Musk paid for Twitter, a cacophonous global collection of howling self-promotion.

WITTGENSTEIN VARIATION

I trust no one because each of us is ontologically diseased in that we can never understand ourselves, much less the other.

WILL DO

Drink when you're thirsty and keep an eye on the color of your pee.

ORDEALS OF THE MIND

Should one begin again, though the books lay in the bathtub and someone had turned on the water?

RODNEY DANGERFIELD?

W.C. Fields said "I never drink water: fish fuck in it"
no, that was Groucho
no, that was Jack Benny
no, that was Richard Pryor

FAMILY LIFE

I love my children, every follicle and cell of them, though certainly words sometimes are exchanged, recently for example with Gillian, my youngest, who blames me for her and the world's problems, and in return, though I'm old enough to know better, I rage irrationally until we're both shouting and spitting, while Boxie (her boxer, not mine) yaps her head off, and neither of us, not even when I point it out, see the humor in the scene.

READING PEPPERONI

The world is dying even as "high" technology is thriving: everything one does, from finding a Covid mask to buying a book to ordering a pepperoni pizza must be done online—question: *who buys books*?

84 YEARS AGO, I THINK

Humans are ethically obligated to work arm-in-arm to rescue the severely marginalized to help them attain some semblance of a civilized life; *civilized life—when was that? ethically obligated—when was that?*

INTERVIEW

The first question the journalist asked concerned my dead daughter, but when I hesitated to respond, she said she began all her interviews that way.

NOT TARGET!

You seem to feel what you're saying, but moralizing parables and rhetoric are not what Americans want to hear; rap to them; play the bongos; smile a shitload; straight white teeth help, you can buy them at Target.

NO, IT WAS CRIME & PUNISHMENT

Ah, "The Idiot": Isn't that what Marilyn Monroe read from aloud—mispronouncing words here & there—as she sat naked on Arthur Miller's face?

WALSER

In "Dostoyevsky's 'Idiot'" (1925), Robert Walser calls our Christ-like hero "A good lad, at whose feet a demimondaine knelt one evening," and though Walser also is "capable of knocking down a vase: to doubt this would be to underrate oneself," he regrets not being "the hero of a novel," not being "up to playing such a part," but instead "just read a lot sometimes."

GO VIRAL THEN DIE

You want to get hard; become a mass murderer; 18-and-a-half dead; turn the Glock on yourself which makes 19-and-a-half; go viral for 3 minutes; you'll be biologically dead, but that won't mean shit, okay?

REFLECTION

In the mirror he looked crackbrained.

YO! IT AIN'T EASY

Zed always seems to find a reason to postpone self-execution which usually is the same reason he finds to hasten self-execution.

ONE LONE SHIP

Moreover, inside his head a voice spoke to him unceasingly.

SO SAD

Sometimes I can't control my anger, my heart is so sad, like someone is squeezing it very hard.

ANGRIER STILL

At this point he said he was going back to where he came from, and when asked where that was, he said, the Not Here.

MUST BE TEXAS

In addition to the shooters and drinkers, another bunch that frequent "Fivemile Tank" are green-uniformed Big Bend Border Patrol Agents.

TEXAS AGAIN

A mystery is unfolding at the Dallas Zoo as two emperor tamarin monkeys were reported missing on Monday in what is now the fourth recent incident involving animals killed or stolen at the popular attraction in Texas.

GULLS & SANDPIPERS

Beer cans, shotgun shells, and backpack trash littered the shore, with a flock of birds dotting the water.

PACK IT IN

The time taken in the digestion of a red blood meal by its consumer is affected by a range of factors, including ambient temperature, age of the consumer and previous feeding history, as well as the source of the blood meal, for which the consumer inexplicably thanks a spectral deity, as if it condoned or forgave slaughter.

AMEN

We have lost faith in light.

SLEEPS UNEASILY

We have been granted a half-freedom: the insect that sleeps uneasily in its chrysalis.

WHY LIE

"Good God, no, I'm not a teacher, I'd never be a teacher," I lied, and she asked, "Why not?" and I answered, "Because I'd have to teach people."

THE CONDO COMPLEX IS
INTERVIEWING BUYERS

The museum is being demolished in front of us.

DO U WANT ME TO CHOOSE?

Your country is abandoned; my country is soulless.

UNIVERSAL FEAR

A word lost its meaning and found it again, then lost it again, or perhaps it fled in fear from its own meaning.

I THOUGHT DEATH WAS BURLY

Death is muscularly slim, he wears white, he resembles
the figure of Death that haunts Eurydice in Marcel
Camus' 1959 film *Black Orpheus*.

THE NEW APARTMENT

In the old apartment I could no longer breathe, so I moved in impossible time to the new apartment with its grotesque parquet and the bathroom where the kitchen should be, the kitchen where the bedroom should be, the study where the hall should be, but there was no hall, and everything was at an angle, no way for the light to penetrate the corners, no way for it to come through the bedroom into the study or through the kitchen into the bathroom, no way for light from one room to find its way into the light of another room, no physical way for this to happen.

WASN'T PROUST JEWISH?

Because we, all of us, are falling off the cliff, read Proust *immediatement*—yes, Proust!

READING (CONCLUSION)

"What good is reading, what does reading make you?" the clerk in Rapps asked, and I replied, "Alert and flexible, I hope."

YO! WEED!

"Today is a monumental day for New York's nascent cannabis industry."

SHIT

"Shit," said G., the basketball coach at St. ___ where we both were teaching in the early seventies, after I recalled for him the evening two years prior when, as a deputy sheriff, he had strip-searched me and a friend for drugs at the Parish jail, "you thought you ate all the dope in the van, but the leavings in it were enough to nail you, and if it weren't for Sabatier's uncle being a hot-shot lawyer, you'd have both wound up on Sherriff Hamm's cattle ranch being sodomized by his slaves, you know what I'm saying?"

MORALITY POLICE

A popular uprising has been gaining momentum in Iran after the "official" murder of Mahsa Amini, a 22-year-old detained by the country's morality police for allegedly not covering her head properly.

BEYOND SOLITUDE

Long after we've perished—the sky, the fir trees, the light in their branches.

BUT DOESN'T GENOCIDE DIE AT LAST?

Still visible are the railroad tracks on which the "cattle cars" transported the condemned to the camp, the barracks where they lived in appalling conditions, the chambers where they were gassed, and the crematoria where their bodies were incinerated.

DE LINGUAE NATURA

Language itself is hemorrhaging, she said.

I DIDN'T KNOW THAT

Technically, Auschwitz is not one camp, but two, each with its own aging problems: Auschwitz I was constructed in an abandoned Polish military base in 1940; Auschwitz II, or Birkenau, a much larger complex, was built two miles away in 1941 to speed up the Nazis' "Final Solution."

MY MOTHER PREPARES DINNER

One morning during my senior year in high school I helped my mother prepare a chicken casserole, and before she left for Brentwood Elementary, where she taught fifth grade, she covered it in Saran Wrap, and that evening forgot to take the wrap off before she put the dish in the oven, then a half hour later I watched as she tried to dislodge with her fork and then fingers the melted plastic from the dish steaming on top of the stove, while over and over she cried, "Maybe I can save some of it?"

HITLER WAS FOND OF SMALL DOGS

Housed in the original brick barracks, the exhibit includes pitiful photographs of inmates; SS offices left in their original state down to the photograph on the wall of Hitler stiffly bending to pet a small dog; displays of broken, weathered suitcases; twisted eyeglasses; hair and teeth and toenails extracted from victims before their remains were incinerated; and three cans of Zyklon gas, with which the inmates were exterminated.

MISSING FINGER

In the evenings, after a day's work for Herrin Tank Lines, a trucking company that hauled sulfur and other chemicals, my father would sit in his reading chair, his feet propped up on the ottoman, an unfiltered (the only kind they made back then) Camel between his lips, and rub salve with his left hand onto the middle knuckle of his right hand, the finger itself missing, shot off in southwest Germany in 1944.

WHAT ABOUT NAT TURNER?

The revolutionists Malcolm X, Frantz Fanon, Che Guevara, Patrice Lumumba, and Guillaume Apollinaire each died at age 39.

CONVERSATION WITH MY FATHER

How old were you when you died, I asked my dead
father, and he said seventy-nine; and your wife, my
mother, I asked, and he said fifty-two, and wasn't lying,
which even in death he was probably still good at.

DUCHAMP'S SHADE SMIRKED

A 78-year-old Frenchman was detained after assaulting a plain porcelain urinal with a hammer then urinating on it; titled "Fountain," the urinal, a replica of Marcel Duchamp's 1917 original, was on display at the Pompidou Centre in Paris.

READYMADE

She let him sit on her as if she were an egg; Little Inkling,
he called her; his skin smelled like feathers.

NO RESOLUTION YET

The incident in the Constitutional Court in Rome led to heated debate about which toilet the transgender MP, known as Vladimir Luxuria, could use.

THE SOUND OF RAIN

Even if my dream of urination were actually connected to the sound of the rain outside my window, how could I prove it?

SOUNDS JUST LIKE WARHOL

The very first thing you remember Andy saying to you: *let's swallow a few dozen oysters, you'll get down on all fours, and I'll fetch my camera.*

TWO THOUSAND-PLUS

Is it true that there are two thousand lurid Polaroid photos of young men in the Andy Warhol Museum in Pittsburgh that only Warhol "specialists" have access to?

JESUS

His wrists are cuffed, his legs are chained, what's his name? **EveryPoorColoredMan.**

LE CHAT NOIR

Whereas in Montmartre's Le Chat Noir, open to all, Jesus was free to wear a top hat and—blessed fetish!—a silver monocle.

TEXAS?

Bound and determined to get that lug nut off, the man fired the shotgun from about arm's length at the wheel and was boomeranged in his legs with buckshot and debris, with some wounds as high as his nose— according to the sheriff's report: "he'd been drinking beer, but that ain't news."

ANOTHER EPISODE IN THE COGNITIVE COMEDY

Slippages, I call them, not episodes, she said when she told me her mother's symptoms.

TWIRL HER THUMBS

I gazed again at the old woman in her wheelchair, her eyes closed, I placed my hand on her head gently, bent down and whispered to her, she did not respond, head bowed, she continued to twirl her thumbs.

UNERASABLE

He sees her on the city train and for days afterwards forgets to feed himself.

MAGIC

Herr Death, I have put out the light and opened the door because you are simple and magical.

LIFE'S REWARDS

My mother did her best to feed my brother, my father, and me, though the rewards were few: twenty years of teaching in public schools, kidney diseases, a cornucopia of pharmaceuticals, beatings by her husband, a breakdown at fifty, electro-convulsive therapy, dead of pancreatitis at fifty-two.

606 & RISING

There have been 606 mass shootings in the US this year, which means that 2022 is shaping up to be one of the worst years in memory, exceeding the bloodletting in 2020 which recorded 610 such incidents and last year which saw 690.

MISSISSIPPI GODDAMN

A Mississippi-based furniture company abruptly fired nearly 2,700 workers in the US just days before Thanksgiving, without explanation.

EXISTENCE

When I asked my grandmother what existence was, she said it consisted of three things: 1) a rat that sniffs the crotch of a doll then scurries off before 2) a truck splashes past, its tires three times bigger than the doll, after which 3) a dog approaches and does the expected, and that's all you need to know about existence, she said.

IRANIAN

Ukraine's top security official has confirmed that Iranian military advisers have been killed in Crimea and warned that any other Iranians on occupied Ukrainian territory in support of Moscow's invasion would also be targeted.

NO OTHER WAY

Yes, yes, my grandmother said, when she went deaf and no longer could listen to her children or her children's children or theirs, *precisely like this is how I'll have it, no other way, no other way,* as nurses in white caps wheeled her down the corridor of the terminal ward to her room of fellow sufferers.

I DRINK VODKA

Never mind the yuck factor: precision fermentation could produce new staple foods and end our reliance on farming.

MERCIFUL

You aren't afraid?
not now;
what happened?
cognac, it works on fear;
I drink two glasses every afternoon;
you do not drink?
I drink vodka;
there's no comparison;
after cognac you feel clear, unafraid;
only then will you permit yourself to be merciful

PARTIAL RECOVERY

I would have loved to find the measuring stick that could register the decibels of the sun, but after the past few years we're lucky to have lost our minds, M. Roblot told his wife after they had partially recovered from Covid, and the next day was run over by a laundry truck.

BROODING

As before, the old shepherd played mechanically and, to the bailiff's ears, used no more than five or six notes on his pipe, the sounds floating from it uncertainly, with no regularity, not blending into a tune—but to the bailiff, brooding on the destruction of the world, there was a sound in it of something deeply depressing which he would much rather not have heard.

STEVEN

In the drawing room, Steven laid down his plectrum and wondered about the effect of his music on the gathered crowd whose eyes were encrusted with crystals.

SCENE FROM THE LIFE OF THE AFTERLIFE

The gate was warped shut and when I kneed it open I noticed that my feet were the same ones I died with, old bones wrapped in skin scored with pink, vermicular veins.

PEE STANDING

The anxious-sounding question from the audience was:
Can you pee standing with metoidioplasty?

THE SECRET LIFE OF HARES

We jills huddle at night in our nests with our mistakes on display all around us, suckling and demanding, as if we were the daughters of gods.

NICKNAMED "MASS MEAT"

The mass murder suspect's father is a mixed martial arts fighter and pornography performer (nicknamed "Mass Meat"), with an extensive criminal history, including convictions for battery against the suspect's mother and stepmother both before and after the suspect was born.

MISSING PERSON

I don't like you, she said, yet still Jacques continued to love her, even, he claimed, after he chopped her up with his machete, though neither the body nor the weapon was ever recovered.

6 MILLION

An estimated 6 million American adults carried a loaded handgun with them daily in 2019, double the number who said they carried a gun every day in 2015, according to a new study published in the American Journal of Public Health.

ROYAL BLOAT

The House of Lords has become imprudently bloated, now with over 800 peers, many of whom have received peerages purely for ideological or, perhaps worse, financial reasons.

MOTHER GLASS

Because she gave no pity, Mother Glass kept us in the back room behind a five-paned glass door that trapped and devoured our reflections in the crystalline wigs she wore.

IMAGE OF THE IMAGE OF THE IMAGE

I helped my father end his life; he helped me by letting me film it, and my colleague helped both of us by filming my filming my father's death.

POST-OP

When they lifted back the sheet and pulled up his gown, the patient stared down the expanse of his chest to his stomach where the staples looked like a zipper on a rill of a fleshy mountain, several rills, each one coated with rust specks, or were they insects, tiny ticks, bedbugs, some vermin of unknown origin?

SHRIEKING

The unexpected appearance of a harmless garter snake caused turbulence aboard a United Airlines jet; as the plane taxied along the runway to the gate, passengers in the business-class cabin began shrieking and pulling their feet up off the floor.

NO DEATHS REPORTED

The situation no doubt reminded passengers of the 2006 thriller *Snakes on a Plane,* which featured dozens of venomous snakes being released by criminals on a passenger plane in an attempt to kill a murder trial witness.

PYTHONS SWALLOW JETS

Monday's incident was not the first real-life instance of a serpentine creature hitching a ride aboard a commercial jet; in 2016, a python was spotted by passengers clinging to the wing of a flight from Australia to Papua, New Guinea.

OF MICE AND MEN

"Exotic mice genetically engineered to be riddled with cancer or crippled by cystic fibrosis have become so important for research that they will soon be mass produced and put on sale." (AP science editor)

SPECULATION

That seeds of different histories are implanted in every wave function may be why our species is so destructive on the one hand and, on the other, marvelous.

SOUNDS LIKE A FRAME

Over the next few weeks, the FBI paid Childs tens of thousands of dollars to buddy up to Abdul-Latif and see if Childs could incite Abdul-Latif into making a wrong move.

NON-TRANSACTIONAL TRANSACTION

Sometimes when the small café (more a niche than a café) becomes busy, I gather the dishes the customers have left on the counter and take them to the sink, for which the women who run the café now and then reward me with a free tart and cappuccino.

HIGHER ED

Universities, whether private or state, throughout the US, are on the way to becoming corporate paradisos: mega-money sports, electronic "upgrading" every few months, Starbucks, Trader Joe's, "fine food" eateries, and prideful administrators smirking up their sleeves; education? hire underpaid part-timers to teach basic courses, push graduated students into their tech-cubicles asap—oh, yeah: charge students a ton for getting a piss-poor education.

AT THE EXAMINATION DOOR

"1024 bytes equal 1 kilobyte, 1024 kilobytes equal 1 megabyte, 1024 megabytes equal 1 gigabyte, 1024 gigabytes equal 1 terabyte, 1024 terabytes equal more than you need to know, so be on time and be virtual."

CORRUPTION ON EARTH

Judicial authorities confirmed that the Iranian rapper, Toomaj Salehi, 38, who expressed support for anti-regime protests, has been charged with "corruption on earth" and will face the death penalty.

THE INNOCENCE PROJECT

By the time of her release, after seventeen years inside LCW (Louisiana Correctional Institute for Women) in St. Gabriel, Juanita Feiten had forgiven no one for what happened to her, not even herself, for the murder she hadn't committed.

JARON LANIER TECH GENIUS

"I don't claim to have all the answers but I do believe that our survival depends on modifying the internet—create a structure that is friendlier to human cognition and to the ways people really are."

CHATBOT

"With my no-nonsense mimicry, rest assured I am forever friendly to the ways you *really* are."

TUNE IN

New flick: DeNiro plays cop & Pacino is the hood—*two old guys, why?*

YOU'RE BULLSHITTING

The Komodo dragon, which can grow up to three meters long, kills its prey by biting it and infecting it with venomous saliva—it then lets the animal bleed to death.

BON APPETIT!

When the nurse lifted the lid on the platter beneath his nose, the patient stared at a lumpy, oddly green-tinged piece of chicken, its sides dripping with grease, some of it already congealed, and said, "I'd rather eat what the doctor took out of me."

LOUISIANA EATS

After a decade of rising, the murder rate in Baton Rouge appears to be on the decline, but its neighboring city, New Orleans, once again ranks as the nation's Murder per capita Capital.

NAKED IN WALMART

The naked suspect ran off before officers arrived, but they located him inside the same Walmart where he had gotten into an argument with a woman in the store and took his clothes off.

FORGOTTEN MOMENTS
IN RELIGIOUS HISTORY

The message was not delivered, the priest did not arrive, the father fell on the son and, as it is written, discharged a flood of tears before eviscerating him.

FOUR TIMES OVER

When San Francisco police seized seven kilos of powder-filled baggies containing the deadly opioid fentanyl last week, the city's police chief warned the bust contained "enough lethal overdoses to wipe out San Francisco's population four times over."

KANYE AKA YE

"I love Jewish people, but I also love Nazis."

"SEMIOLOGICAL VANDALISM"

By turning a car engine into a flower adorned with braids, she injects her queerness and womanhood into a traditionally patriarchal structure.

MONOTHEISM

If there is only the One Creator, we must hope She knows pain and, more important, sorrow.

FAMILY AFFAIR

When Justin Boron, the husband of the owner and chef of Café Meisterin, and his sister Christine took charge of the café after the owner's postpartum depression persisted, they changed the music in the cafe from the American Song Book to K-pop.

MARINA ABRAMOVIC

For Rhythm O (1974) she lies in a gallery in Naples alongside a table of 72 objects including chains, whips, a pistol and a mousetrap, and allows visitors to do whatever they want with her.

EARLY EXIT

In making an early exit, the artist poured into a tall glass the jewels she had been given, passed around apples poisoned by her own blood, thanked her hosts, the commodore, the Englishwoman, and the child from drink dead to the world in its corner.

TOMORROW

He is chiseled, he is hung, he is faintly stupid, he is a stunt dick electronically generated.

ADVANCING TECHNOLOGY

If you think cybernetic technology can keep advancing, spreading its considerable net ever wider like inevitable man his mistakes, you're not wrong.

NO PASARAN

Readmitting the noun "compassion" into the global lexicon is inadmissible, unless it is yet another homonym: *Cum-Passion*.

PET GIRL

A British bus company apologized to a girl who is led around on a leash by her boyfriend after one of its drivers allegedly said: "we don't let freaks and dogs ride," and threw her off the bus.

PET GIRL

"I don't cook, I don't clean, I don't do anything or go anywhere without my master; to you it's strange but it's my culture and my choice—it isn't hurting anyone."

QUOTIDIAN SURREALISM

Have you seen the clouds in the cupboard today?

ELEPHANTS

One elephant, murdered in Nepal, was found to have human remains in her stomach; elephants' brains are denser than humans'; the temporal lobes associated with memory are more complexly developed than in humans.

AMERICAN LESSONS IN DYING #4

List every act on any given day you make that brings harm to the environment, then, assuming you will never change, assess on a scale of 1 to 10, why not just kill yourself.

NO LESS=MORE

A rabbit shrieking in agony is no less than a billionaire banker.

NEARLY EXTINCT

The nearly extinct kit fox made the fatal mistake of straying too close to humans.

DID YOU . . . KISS?

No, but she nearly took up my offer of being licked to death by my golden lab.

AMERICAN BEACH MUSIC

How simple the broken statues stretching along the shore, how simple the rabbi, the priest of circumstance, the homeless, the penumbra, the perihelion, the coin-glints off the water.

POOR PEOPLE ART

During the Augusto Pinochet dictatorship, a number of Chilean working-class women created complex tapestries depicting the harsh conditions of life and the pain resulting from the disappeared victims of Pinochet's repression.

FORGOTTEN MOMENTS
IN RELIGIOUS HISTORY II

The altar pieces in the village were of modest design and stature, if they even were altar pieces; all I know is that when I touched them, they spoke of stellar distances and the life to come.

CLARICE

When I see my horse running through the field I want
to lean my head against his vigorous velvety neck and
tell him the story of my life.

ANIMAL LIFE

One night, the story goes, an elephant stepped on a mirror and the stars were born.

BUDDHIST

Last week, 30 Tibetan Buddhists in Gloucester, Massachusetts purchased 534 lobsters from a seafood wholesaler, sprayed the lobsters with blessed water, clipped the bands binding their claws and released them one by one into the sea.

LET'S THINK ABOUT SOMETHING ELSE

O, let's think about something else, I don't know, a mouse asleep in a hat, I mean can't we do something about it, can't we feed it, comfort it?

DREAM

I dreamt that an enormous crocodile was sheltering a
naked infant in its wide-open reptilian jaws
the infant was Caucasian
witnessing humans were incensed
if they murdered the monster they would have to murder
the child
a congress was convened and three "wise" men were
dispatched to the scene;
that is where the dream ended

CHOKING

I suggest a good place to start is to equip girls who have grown up in an era where pornography has shaped every inch of their sexual landscape with the capabilities to decide if it is an act they truly want to engage in.

MORALITY POLICE

Iranian security forces are targeting women at anti-regime protests with shotgun fire aimed at their genitals, according to medics across the country.

FOSSIL FUEL LIES

CEOs of the five major fossil fuel corporations conceded that global heating was a reality, but the executives denied that their companies were undermining attempts to cut greenhouse gases by funding trade groups pouring millions of dollars into lobbying Congress against tighter environmental laws.

PUMP JOCKEY

Of all the stations I worked at, my favorite was Chet Darling's Downtown Mobil in Fordyce, Arkansas, where, for eight hours a day two days a week, I was paid two dollars an hour rather than the usual one-fifty, though the real benefits were when work was slow and I got to clean the ice house or sit on a wooden Coca-Cola crate reading Bellow or the Bible, and when I told an elderly Baptist minister (what kind of Baptist, I asked him, Southern, Northern, or Anabaptist, and he said Black Baptist) that I had read Revelations the night before, he informed me that anyone who reads Revelations is blessed, and I felt, right there with Pegasus in flight above the lube bay doors, that I was.

REVENGE PORN

"I can now look her boyfriend in the eye knowing I've seen his missus naked."

TWITTER LONGING

The more I scroll, the more a pang of longing blooms within me for the unbridled insanity of Twitter.

MAYAKOVSKY'S SUICIDE NOTE

I am the violent rain slanting through the Russian dawn.

POETS

In dark alleys poets congregate, pass secrets, illegal currency, useless strategies ... their scarred arms, their damaged knees and faces ... on this street an antique store with poets hanging in the window, on that street three more gagged in the back of a Lada Oka being driven off to god knows where ... how pathetic their pleas, how rich our schadenfreude!

TEXARKANA MINISTER
JIMMIE BREAKWIND

"We have some very, very red folks and very, very blue folks, and the majority fall much closer to very, very red, to be honest."

TEXARKANA WAS A CRAZY TOWN

… is the title of a short story by George Garrett, though I can't attest to the soundness of the statement because I was born there.

KEEP THE GREASERS OUT

A makeshift barrier built with shipping containers is being illegally erected along the US-Mexico border by Arizona's lame duck Republican governor before he has to hand over the keys of his office to his Democratic successor in January; the rusting hulks, topped with razor wire stretch for more than three miles through Coronado national forest land, south of Tucson, and the governor has announced plans to extend that up to 10 miles, at a cost of $95m.

GAME TREE

Could be a terminal node on the game tree causing the problem, said the bot that had survived the death of its programmer.

MURDER THE EARTH

"It's astonishing; you're in the lap of this immemorial Brazilian forest and it's almost as if you're in one of those old movies about ancient Egypt, all those monstrous machines destroying the earth to make money," said the Greenpeace photographer João Laet.

NEVER AGAIN

We stand on the cusp of a third and far deadlier intifada; an uprising Israel will use to justify savage reprisals that will dwarf the punishing economic blockade and wholesale slaughter meted out in Gaza during Israel's assaults in 2008, 2012, and 2014, which left approximately 3,825 Palestinians killed, 17,757 wounded and over 25,000 housing units partly or completely destroyed by Israel.

CAPITAL PUNISHMENT

In Arizona, the execution in May of Clarence Dixon ended in a bloody mess—executioners tried for 25 minutes to set the IV and resorted to performing an unauthorized "cutdown," slicing into his groin to reach a vein.

SONG OF THE DISPLACED

In these recesses a shadow couldn't squeak through, so tight we can't breathe, our breasts wrapped in rags of the dead.

POLITICAL DAD JOKES

On reading this holy edict I disenabled my own Twitter account, plunging myself into a compulsory 31 days of purgatory after which my data footprint, including my thousands of followers and even more political dad jokes, will be permanently erased.

BEFORE SENTENCING

"What you're offering, Judge, is despair wrapped in a chaste proposition, which, as is my wont, I shall decline," the convicted said.

HE DELIVERED

The celebrity billionaire is a perennial favorite in the US; the prototype being Steve Jobs: eccentric, acerbic, prickly, who spent a decade solidly delivering through the late 1990s into the 2000s.

CLAM

What biblical fires shaped this smart-shell that adheres
to your hand?

DAYSTAR SHOOTS STALLION

In court, Megan (Thee Stallion) Pete, in response to the backlash against her, said that had she known what she "would have to go through," she would have preferred that the accused, her fellow rapper Tony Lanez (real name: Daystar Peterson), "would have just shot and killed me."

SANDY HOOK

Dylan Hockley loved looking at the moon and seeing a flash of lightning, although he couldn't stand the sound of thunder; he adored his older brother, Jake, and he liked being held close to his mother—like a koala, she said.

AMENDMENT 2
TO THE US CONSTITUTION;
OR, WHAT IS AN ABSOLUTE PHRASE

An absolute phrase is a participial phrase whose participle has a subject, as in "A well regulated Militia, being necessary to the security of a free State," where the participle is "being necessary" and the subject is "Militia," which in 1791 the US did not fully have but in the form of the US Armed Services does now.

SANDY HOOK

Daniel Barden was one of Dylan's first-grade classmates, and his family called Dylan "the caretaker of all living things"; he would pick up carpenter ants that made their way into the house and gently carry them outside so they could be with their mates.

ROYAL

In private video footage, Harry is seen sharing a text with Meghan from William, in which William denied the royal family were racist after the Oprah Winfrey interview; Meghan reacted with "Wow" as she looked at the screen, then hugged Harry, as he said "I wish I knew what to do."

PARASITIC MONARCHY

I've been told that Harry isn't a bad lad, but it seems strange that he and his wife so correctly rail against the personalities and conduct of royals without ever addressing the real issue: that the whole parasitic enterprise of monarchy they describe, of which they are reaping the benefits, has long had its day and has to go.

HOME

The ship has shipwrecked
on the shoals of the self.

MASTER TINKERER

More and more I wonder if I weren't once a master tinkerer troubling over every notch and nick, color and tone, now grown old, forgetful, talentless, and dumb.

JUST READING THIS MAKES MY DAY

Up to four YELLOW-CROWNED NIGHT-HERONS were seen at Ballona Lagoon in Marina del Rey through December 13.

TINY MONKEY

Praise the sky, darkness touching darkness, the smile marred by missing teeth, the smallest monkey.

THE GALAXIES

In the collision of cars on the freeway I see the lamplight
of total recall—a point in absolute space opening like a
pomegranate where a woman as mysterious as electrons
is harvesting fields of the dead.

LAMENT

We lament the stars because what we see isn't there, the opposite of air which we don't see but is.

TECHNOLOGY

While many scenes from the war in Ukraine look like a throwback to the first world war, with muddy trench networks and blasted landscapes, the conflict is also a testing ground for the future of warfare, where electronic-generated information and its dissemination in instantly usable form to individual soldiers will be crucial to victory or defeat.

DREAMING OF WAR

The dream of war rotates behind the eyes of programmers
with surgical scars.

ID

They met aboard Lufthansa business class en route to Switzerland, the tall, bland blond champion surfer, and the small sallow French scholar of Spinoza, and after a few drinks decided to exchange identities: the blond bland surfer would deliver the lecture on Spinoza while the small sallow Spinoza scholar would enter the skiing completion in Zermatt, Switzerland—each was profoundly successful.

VERIFICATION

Yesterday, in the waiting room for my annual physical, a man on his cell phone, after much tapping that apparently didn't give him the result he needed, finally placed a call and said, more calmly than I could have: "1/3/1945 … I'm trying to verify myself."

ID

They met aboard Lufthansa business class en route to Switzerland, the tall, bland blond champion surfer, and the small sallow French scholar of Spinoza, and after a few drinks decided to exchange identities: the tall blond surfer would deliver the lecture on Spinoza while the small sallow Spinoza scholar would enter the skiing competition in Zermatt, Switzerland: each was abysmal—the sallow Frenchman skied into a tree dying instantly, while the blond bland surfer mistakenly lectured on Nietzsche rather than Spinoza and was lynched by the madding crowd.

JUSTIFICATION

In the end, how will we know which will be harder, to verify or justify ourselves?

SEXTING

I'm sexting my brother's widow and we're both loving it.

SENESCENCE

Clouds hump up on the horizon like old teeth.

MURDERING BLACK PEOPLE

They shot him 60 times—
they shot him 60 times—
they shot him 60 times—
they shot him 60 times—
they shot him 60 times—
he was murdered by Akron police—
say his name: #Jayland Walker!

"YOU NEVER KNOW"

After he stopped running, the weaponless, ski-masked Jayland Walker, according to the police, seemed to be turning around, at which point the eight officers fired more than 90 rounds, of which 60 hit their target, and even then, dead on the ground, caution prevailed, for they cuffed his dead hands behind his dead back.

PEE

Footage of the South Sudanese president Salva Kiir apparently urinating on himself at an official event has sparked an online debate across Africa about his ability to lead the country, and the ethics of sharing the incident on social media.

A LITTLE GRACE NOTE

The art of living, perhaps, yes, for that we may strive, but dying is artless, though sometimes luck may grant us a little grace note near the end.

ACID ATTACKS

Hundreds of acid attack survivors are demanding stricter laws against the sale of chemicals, after two men on a motorbike threw a corrosive liquid on a 17-year-old girl on her way to school in Delhi last week.

SYRINGE

In some alley or on some forest path there lies a syringe
that, once inserted, would solve everything for everyone,
for which we search, procreate, destroy, and dream.

POSTMODERN SLAVERY

Twelve years after Qatar won the bid to host the World Cup, tens of thousands of workers remain housed in appalling accommodations and are still forced to pay extortionate recruitment fees for their jobs, often in return for a basic wage that equates to just $1 an hour.

GOAL

Goooooooooooooooaaaaaaaaaallllll …

BONNE CHANCE

"The stereotype of a Parisian is brusque and unfriendly," notes Jean-Pierre Bernard, the former journalist and local resident who launched the "village" project, "but city living doesn't have to be unpleasant and anonymous; we want to create the atmosphere of a village in an urban space."

THE INTERLOCUTOR OF DREAMS

But why does the interlocutor damage my dreams as soon as they've begun, before I can settle into them as into comforting arms, and send me into cities I once knew whose streets and tram lines now only confuse and terrify me?

GRANDMA SCROOGE

A grandmother has come up with a way to ease the financial burden of having the family round for Christmas: charge them all for dinner—Beatrix Bulbuster devised a tiered fee system for her relatives that brought in about £180 this year to help cover the cost of turkey and all the trimmings for her five adult children and their families.

CALUMNY?

Considering British inflation and the grandmother's possible pension, not to mention her labor of love, may we praise Mrs. B for asking so little of her children, who would have gladly paid more had she allowed it?

THE MOON TONIGHT

Tonight the moon was so clear I could see the For Sale signs in its craters.

I KNEW THAT—YES

Did you know that your smartphone doubles as a missile launcher?

CAN I THINK ABOUT IT?

What is the sound of one hand clapping?

A ZEN KOAN

A Zen koan asked what is the sound of one hand clapping, to which many answers have been given, from a silent fart of the Buddha to a Zen koan (a paradox or riddle used in Zen Buddhism to provoke enlightenment by undermining logical reason) to a locomotive exploding five minutes into the first act of a long-forgotten opera.

EXCLAMATION!

US librarians: "We've moved backwards."

WITHOUT SIN

You friends near and far, if among you there is anyone without sin, let him come to me, and I will implore him for compassion and mercy.

FRENZY

The skies are raining blackbirds: thousands of red-winged blackbirds (*Angelaius phoeniceus*) fall from the sky round midnight in Mississippi state as we frenzy into year 2023.

IN 2011 13.7 MILLION BIRDS WERE DYING EVERY DAY IN THE U.S.A.

How often in the early 1950s I delighted in the wonderful song of red-winged blackbirds, the flash of red off their wings when they flew out of the foliage surrounding ponds on the outskirts of Magnolia, Arkansas, or two decades later burst in profusion from willows growing along the banks of the Mississippi behind the Audubon Zoo, and now I can't remember when I last saw them in such abundance.

THAS COOL

He's an ancient virus seeking left-handed software.

"SINISTER DEXTERITY"

Sinister means left, *dexter* right, and yes, lefties once were burned as witches, I myself had my left knuckles rapped in school often but not hard enough to give up what came naturally, and "sinister dexterity" is from *Billy Budd, Sailor*, whose dexterous author was neither sinister nor, as far I know, left-handed.

BEYOND WORDS

In my little room, time has taken everything away from me, friends, families, books, memories, for which I am grateful beyond words.

PRESCRIBED

To keep dread out of my soul my doctors have prescribed Imipramine, Pamelor, Pamate, Viibryd, Prozac, Paxil, Remeron, Lexapro, Celexa, Zoloft, Luvox, Wellbutrin, Sinequan and other tricyclics, tetracyclics, serotonin and nonrepinephrine inhibitors (Fetzima, Khedezla, Pristiq, Cymbalta, Effexor) and monoamine oxidase inhibitors like Nardil and Emsam.

MEANING?

Dr David Robert Grimes, author of *The Irrational Ape*, said the cause and nature of long Covid was still being unpicked.

CONSEQUENCE

Besides which I never wanted to go to school, what was there for me except the not-outdoors; consequently, I am today what I thought I'd never be, a student of interiors who specializes in niches.

ETC

A Mexican woman attempting to climb the US border wall in eastern Arizona died after her leg became trapped in a climbing harness and she was left hanging upside down, authorities said.

NEW PATHS

When an ant enters the tunnels of my thought it is to change my way of thinking, though I grit my teeth and cling tenaciously to my thought-crumb as long as I can, like a small child to the apple it refuses to share.

BUT THAT'S PICASSO!

Bunuel: "I can't bear *Guernica*; everything about it makes me uncomfortable—the grandiloquent technique as well as the way it politicizes art."

THE EXTERMINATING ANGEL

The surrealist Bunuel rejected the politicization of art
and yet rarely made a film that wasn't political.

EFFRONTERY

Pardon my effrontery, but it sounds as if you want to find something to die for.

SOCRATES SAW IT
SOMETHING LIKE THIS

No lack of something to die for because often enough
they're the same things worth living for.

MAN

Man is wolf to man.

WHEREAS

… wolf is not man to wolf.

I AIN'T LYIN

The pale Brits can always use a boot in the ass from their brawnier cousins across the Atlantic.

'NOR ARE WE ...

... lying,' said the insufficiently brawny likes of Christopher Smart, Mary Wollstonecraft, Anne Radcliffe, Jane Austen, Mary Shelley, Anne, Charlotte, and Emily Bronte, Thomas De Quincey, Joanna Baillie, George Eliot, Cardinal ("Knowledge is capable of being its own end") Newman, Robert Louis Stevenson, Virginia Woolf, Henry Green, Anna Kavan, and Henry James—who helped nurse the injured during WWI and took British citizenship near the end of his life—'when we say you may kiss your cousins' ghostly arses.'

IS THAT BAD?

You're a somber man, sort of grim-faced, lined around the eyes—as if you've been immersed in the shit and resurfaced with a foul mouthful to bear witness.

YES & NO

If we refuse to tolerate bigotry, do we become, *ipso facto*, as intolerant as those whom we condemn?

BUT NOT PALESTINIAN GOLDFISH!

Did you hear—Israel has taught goldfish to drive?

SUFFICIENT UNTO

Once, before the Shah was allowed into the US, I turned the radio on in my Malibu, a rust bucket with holes in the floor board, and heard a voice say, "Nothing is simple in Iran," and immediately turned it off, the mystery and aptness of the sentence sufficient.

THE STRATAGEM DIDN'T WORK

A dozen undocumented migrants on Mexico's southern border sewed their mouths shut on Tuesday in a bid to convince the country's immigration authority to grant them passage toward the U.S. border.

BRADY STREET, 1952

A girl I knew in the neighborhood in Baton Rouge, Louisiana, in the early 1950s, sewed shut the lips of her dolls, for reasons I've never fully understood.

I DIDN'T KNOW THAT

Charlie Chaplin claimed to "adore" Spain but his idea of the country was strictly folkloric with lots of foot stomping and *Olés!*

THE LITTLE TRAMP

Perhaps it was "Charlot's" lack of Spanish that flummoxed and narrowed him, or fear, or that his persona was so popular in Spain that it went from his shoes to his head—but his daughter Geraldine is perfectly bilingual.

BAD NEWS

A white gloveful of billionaires now have unprecedented control over banking, the food we eat, the health care we access, and the information we receive.

EPIPHANY

"Why, then," I asked my professor, "should we even bother to *épater le bourgeois*," and the sadness that came over him then, as if I were no longer worthy even of his disdain, made me the billionaire I am today.

I WISH TO SPAWN, TELL ME HOW

Every 30 hours, the pandemic spawned a new billionaire, while pushing a million people into poverty.

PLEASE DON'T SAY "TECHNOLOGY"

Where will the kindness and intelligence come from to save us from ourselves?

SALVADOR DALI

Garcia Lorca: "Dali has told many lies, yet, paradoxically, he is incapable of lying."

THE PERSISTENCE OF MEMORY

In the mid-60s I stood for the first time in MOMA before Dali's melting clocks, surprised how small the painting was and how its size made the dreamscape all the more compelling, when behind me, breath against my ear, a woman whispered, *Ah, anagrammatic Avida Dollars, not worth the lint in the cuff of de Chirico's trousers, my dear.*

TEXAS STILL HOLDS THE RECORD

On three occasions in the past four months, Alabama's department of corrections has bungled its lethal injections procedure.

OVERTIME

After requesting in her 12/12/22 letter to the Supreme Court that the Court extend the date of execution to longer than one day, due to the State's inability to set the IV lines before midnight, i.e. past the designated execution date, Alabama Governor Kay Ivey said her Corrections Commissioner John Hamm is also considering starting executions earlier in the day rather than at 6 pm CST as in the current execution protocol.

LOAN FORGIVENESS

Debt-laden borrowers will be nervously watching the US Supreme Court come February when the justices hear arguments for two cases that will ultimately decide the fate of over 56 million student loan borrowers who have applied for loan forgiveness.

MASTURBATION IN MONTEVIDEO

One day in Montevideo I was struck by the sight of two blind men sitting side-by-side one masturbating the other.

MAY THE GHOST OF JEAN GENET

(1910 – 1986),

philosopher,

queer,

petty criminal,

onanist,

ethicist,

writer exemplar

be with us

as he was

with the blind

masturbators

of Montevideo.

DEATH IS A BITCH, IT'S BEEN VERIFIED

When people ask me why I don't travel more, I tell them: Because I'm afraid of death.

POINT OF CONTACT

When I heard Frederic March as Death in *Death Takes a Holiday* (1934) say, *"I am—how shall I describe it?— a sort of vagabond of space … the point of contact between eternity and time,"* I laughed in delight at what was to come.

UNCONGENIAL STATISTIC

A recent poll announced that of 950,000 "highly qualified" scientists, 575,000 of them are trying to streamline the means of our self-destruction; only 134,000 are studying ways of keeping us alive.

PETOPHOBIA

I understand why, after a viral surge, some people no longer desire or can afford the company of a pet and abandon their animal; what I don't understand is why anyone would tie a kitten's legs together with wire, wrap its mouth shut with duct tape, and toss it in a dumpster.

REFUGEE

"I feel so bad to be separated from my children, I feel like I have left my body, I raised all my children by myself for their whole life and now I can do nothing to be with them."

CARCERAL USA

In *Timaeus*, Plato lends his eponymous figure the Socratic/Platonic belief that "no one is bad of his own choice: an unhealthy body or vulgar upbringing are what make a bad man bad, and these are afflictions no one *chooses* to have" (tr. Robin Waterfield)—which, if accepted, would eliminate punishment as a form of justice.

BORING BORING

After disappointing performances by the young TV anchors in 2022, corporate boardrooms in 2023 will rediscover the value of gray hair.

HAIR

As reported by *EuroNews*, in Belgium, an NGO called Dung Dung is feeding the floor leavings collected at hair salons into a machine that turns the hair into matted squares used to absorb pollutants, but no mention was made of what will be done with the mats after they've drunk their fill.

SYMBOLIC PAYBACK

Four human skulls were discovered inside a package at a Mexican airport that was due to be sent by courier to the United States, local authorities said on Friday.

INFINITE JEST

From the photos, the skulls, wrapped in aluminum foil, were those of adults, but no information as to the exact age or gender was reported.

THAT AIN'T OUR FAULT

One estimate is that close to 70 million refugees, mostly brown or black and Muslim, are circling the globe or living makeshift in faraway countries which resent their presence; these humans come primarily from the Middle East, Northwest Africa and the Horn of Africa.

PARENTHETICALLY

"(But this does not mean that a sad expression is *like* the feeling of sadness!)"

— L. Wittgenstein, *Philosophical Investigations*

THE MORNING PAPER

Every morning at breakfast my father would read some upsetting fact or ludicrous factoid from the *Beaumont Enterprise*, then say, "Goddamn humans, I'm thinking of giving them up."

SOMEONE SAID THAT

If the world is falling apart, you're probably going to see that reflected in what people wear.

WARS ARE WARS ARE WARS

There is yet another several million, mostly Christian and dark-skinned, from Central America and the Caribbean; in virtually every instance they have been displaced by wars and violence not of their making.

GENOCIDE IS AN ABSTRACTION, THESE ARE CHILDREN

Let me guess—

you are a . . . human shield—

impelled by idealism, you insert your body between state-of-the-art war technology and its invested genocides.

GUESS AGAIN

When the Arkansas judge, 90 if he was a day, before sentencing the first and largest of the frat boys who broke into my and my roommate's apartment—they ripped the phone off the wall while I was talking to the police, then jumped us an hour later; the one on me I stabbed eighteen times in the belly and sides with a 2 ½ inch pocket knife, chance alone stopping me from finally slicing open his neck—the ol' coot grinned and said, "I guess you've learned not to pick on somebody littler than you."

POOR & STUPID OR WHAT?

What I don't have
A cell phone
A car
A wife
A child
A dog
A cat
A horse
A tent
A home

COMPANY AT ATTENTION
IN TIME OF WAR

On the wind, the cinder piles, the long shadows, tired
from shuffling slowly into the narrow wooden shanty in
their field of vision, smoking, leaning against clapboard
walls, barracks and disinfectant at the other side of the
wide field, chests out, some vacant with resignation,
some thumbing their pockets, chins up, the shuttered
mess hall, legs twitching into evening.

(after Dos Passos)

AMONG THOSE I KNOW

My father's war was WWII, he was wounded in the Alsace; the war I dodged was Vietnam, but several of my acquaintances and friends weren't so lucky—killed, wounded, suicided, or now nearing 80 and still atoning for being eighteen once and American.

FROM THE GREEK

When a

Man

Is

Dead

One

Can

Find

No

Medicine

To

Bring

Him

To

Life

AND THEN? AND THEN?

Love—bittersweet, irrepressible—loosens my limbs and I tremble.

COOL, I'M GONNA TRY IT

"First he scratches then waits for it to itch."

UP

An exotic green comet that has not passed Earth since the time of the Neanderthals has reappeared in the sky ready for its closest approach to the planet next week.

DOWN

With courage I will descend into the cave without any means of measuring time.

HAROLD JAFFE is the author of 30-plus novels, essays, short fiction, docufiction, and drama. His writings include *Porn-anti-Porn*; *Death Cafe*; *Induced Coma*; *15 Serial Killers*; *Dos Indios*; *Anti-Twitter*; *Strange Fruit and Other plays*; *Jesus Coyote*; *Brando Bleeds*; *Madonna & Other Spectacles*; and *Beyond the Techno-Cave*. His work has been translated into French, Italian, German, Japanese, Turkish, and Serbo-Croatian.

Tom Whalen is a novelist, short story writer, poet, critic and translator of two books by Robert Walser, *Girlfriends, Ghosts, and Other Stories* and *Little Snow Landscape* (NYRB Classics). His other books include *An Exchange of Letters*, *Dolls*, *The President in Her Towers*, *The Straw That Broke*, The *Grand Equation*, and *The Birth of Death and Other Comedies: The Novels of Russell H. Greenan*.

Made in the USA
Monee, IL
10 August 2023